A Princess and Her Garden

A Princess and Her Garden

A Fable of Awakening and Arrival

PATRICIA R. ADSON, Ph.D.

CAPT®

Center for Applications of Psychological Type, Inc. ∣ 2815 NW 13th St., Suite 401 ∣ Gainesville, FL 32609 ∣ 1.800.877.2278

A Princess and Her Garden
A Fable of Awakening and Arrival
First Edition, 1999
Second Edition, 2011

Text ©1999, 2011 Patricia R. Adson, Ph.D.
Illustrations ©2011 Center for Applications of Psychological Type, Inc.
Original illustrations—Barbara Beshoar
Book design—John Amerson
Journal co-author—Jennifer E. Van Homer

Published by
Center for Applications of Psychological Type (CAPT), Inc.
2815 NW 13th St., Suite 401
Gainesville, FL 32609
Printed in China

Printed with permission from Many Rivers Press,
www.davidwhyte.com. David Whyte, "The Journey," from *River Flow*
©Many Rivers Press, Langley, Washington.

Library of Congress Cataloging-in-Publication Data

Adson, Patricia R.
A princess and her garden : a fable of awakening and arrival /
Patricia R. Adson. -- 2nd ed.
p. cm.
ISBN 978-0-935652-93-2 (hardcover)
1. Self-perception--Juvenile literature. 2. Helplessness
(Psychology)--Juvenile literature. I. Title.
BF697.5.S43A37 2011
158.1--dc23
2011025691

For my clients who taught
me this story and who continue to
care for the gardens within.

Sometimes with
the bones of the black
sticks left when the fire
has gone out

someone has written
something new
in the ashes
of your life.

You are not leaving.
Even as the light
fades quickly.
You are arriving.

From "The Journey" by David Whyte

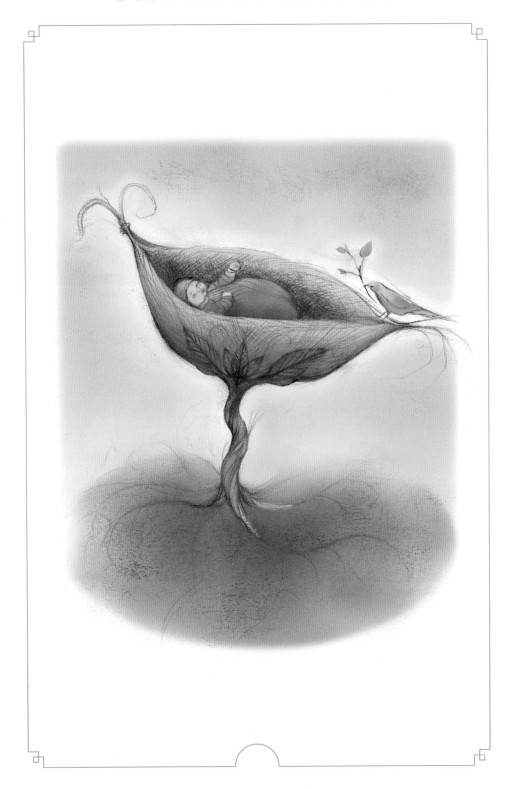

pon her birth the tiny princess was
given a garden—a birthright —
carefully prepared, fertilized and seeded with
everything she would ever need in all the years
to come. This perfect garden awaited only tender,
gentle care and protection until the day when
she would be able to care for it herself.

At first, the small and helpless Princess had to
depend on the King and Queen to care for her
garden. All she could do was to let them know
that something needed to be done.

Gradually, as the princess grew, she became aware
of the beauty of her special piece of land and
realized that the King and the Queen appeared
in her garden whenever she summoned them.
She began to believe that both the land and the
people belonged to her. In this way she lived there
happily for quite some time.

I am a Princess
and this is my land.
These people belong to me.
I must be the Princess of Other People.

s time went by and the Princess had grown old enough to venture out of her garden, she discovered that the King and the Queen had gardens of their own and a castle keep wherein they stored the gardening supplies and tools.

As soon as the King and the Queen realized that the Princess was old enough to explore their domains, they began to demand that she care for their gardens in exchange for their caring for hers. No longer did they appear at her every call. Instead, they expected her to answer their calls and often they withheld her gardening supplies and tools until she did as they commanded. To her dismay, the Princess began to doubt that the King and the Queen belonged to her and wondered if perhaps she might belong to them!

I wonder what has changed
and what I am supposed to do.

ne day the Princess wondered if she had been careless, for the King deliberately trampled some delicate plants in her garden. That night she heard the grinding sounds of the quarreling voices of the King and the Queen and she ran to her garden to hide. The Queen, however, found the Princess and scolded her, covered her with shame, then forced her to return to their gardens to care for them whilst her own garden lay fallow.

I must be very bad.
What have I done to make them so angry?
It is all my fault.
I must be careful to learn how to
make them happy
or they will not take care of my garden.

From that day on, the Princess knew that in order to entice the King and the Queen to care for her garden she must determine exactly how they wanted her to take care of each of their gardens. Her fears about losing her powers lessened as she found that she had the power to make them happy, sad or angry by the ways in which she tended to their gardens. She discovered, as well, that when she made the King and the Queen happy her own garden thrived, but when they were angry or sad, portions of her garden died. The Princess learned to be very, very careful when working in the gardens of the King and the Queen.

nd thus for many years the Princess continued to toil, striving to regain the magic and the power of the time when she had been so capable of making the King and the Queen happy; when she had truly been the Princess of Other People and the Other People had been caring and loving, not angry and critical. At long last the tireless work of the Princess created gardens of incredible beauty for the King and the Queen. Soon, people came from miles around to admire these gardens and to praise the King and the Queen for raising such a talented gardener.

> *Look how my garden thrives*
> *when I do as they want.*
> *Now I have learned my job.*
> *I am the Princess of Other People*
> *after all—*
> *their happiness and mine are*
> *intertwined in our gardens.*

ne day a Prince from a distant land visited these magnificent gardens and, dazzled by their beauty, sought the hand of the Princess. The Princess was elated, for surely a person who prized her handiwork would allow her to make him happy and would, in turn, care for her garden.

And so, the Princess married the Prince, and for many a day it seemed that all of her wishes had come true. The Princess made very few mistakes and tended most carefully to the garden of the Prince. He, in turn, cared for her garden. Life was wonderful for both.

I am once again in charge of a kingdom.
This is the way that it works:
I care for his garden
and he cares for mine
and we will live happily ever after.

fter a while, however, the Princess began to wonder if she had lost her powers, for the Prince began to neglect her garden. Soon he began to berate and criticize her. Again her garden failed to thrive. Now the frantic Princess spent all of her time trying to figure out what she was doing wrong. She worked harder and harder and harder. But once more the Princess of Other People failed to please.

I've done it again.
I am a failure,
if only I knew more.
I have lost my power to make others happy
and now know only how to make
them sad and angry.
It is all my fault.
I am not a very good Princess.

In her despair the Princess turned to her Ladies-in-Waiting who, to her surprise, received her with warmth and understanding. The Ladies-in-Waiting had heard similar stories before and insisted that she had done nothing wrong. Although they were gentle and kind to her, they became enraged when they heard of the actions of the Prince. The Ladies-in-Waiting explained that the Prince was the one at fault. They offered to arm the Princess immediately and to help her do battle with the Prince and with the King and Queen.

he Princess was stunned. She could not believe it was not her fault. She was sure the Prince would change his ways if only he understood what he was supposed to do. She declined their offer of arms and raced off to find the Prince and tell him what she had learned.

Surely when he understands
that I did the best I could
and I am willing to keep trying,
he will change and give me another chance.

o her great dismay, however, she found the Prince in the garden of another. On so doing she knew at once that he would never understand—or even try to understand. Her tears of sadness and betrayal quickly turned to anger and she returned to her Ladies-in-Waiting, ready at last to hear their advice and to accept their offer of weapons.

Now, armed and angry, the Princess lashed out and destroyed the beautiful garden she had created for the Prince. Remembering also the words of the Ladies-in-Waiting, the Princess returned to the gardens of the King and the Queen and trampled parts of their gardens as well.

For a brief time the Princess felt justified and powerful as she remembered the many ways in which the King, the Queen and the Prince had devastated her garden. Those memories fueled her fury and she was smugly satisfied with her ability to retaliate.

I may no longer be able to please them
or even to make them understand.
But, I still have the power
to make them angry and sad!

nfortunately, in a very short while, all of her satisfaction drained away and the Princess was filled with a vast emptiness. "What now?" she asked herself as she returned to her own parched and wilted garden. "How can I ever find anyone to care for me now? I have tried everything: I tried to learn, I tried to listen, I tried remaining silent, I tried fighting, I tried to make them understand. Nothing has worked."

In sorrow and bewilderment the Princess wandered alone, seeking someone who might help her to make others understand and appreciate her and care for her garden again.

I am a failure and I shall never find
the one whose garden I can care for,
and who, in turn, will care for mine.

t long last the lonely Princess found a Wise Woman Wizard and implored her to help. The Wizard surveyed the blighted garden and immediately offered aid. First, the Wizard unlocked her own gardening shed and brought out an amazing array of tools and equipment. Next, she taught the Princess to analyze the soil to determine its need for moisture and nutrients. Finally, she helped the Princess to build a fence around her garden, and presented to her the one-and-only key to the gate.

I'm not sure what the Wizard is doing.
She is taking good care of me,
but she doesn't seem to be teaching me
how to take care of her.

As the Wizard prepared to leave, the Princess protested. She did not want to care for her own garden. This was not what she had sought. She wanted someone to teach her how to get others to care for her garden. Hadn't she made that clear?

The Princess was angry, disappointed and fearful, convinced that once again she had failed. Furthermore, the Wizard had never even allowed the Princess of Other People to display her talents by caring for the garden of the Wizard. In fact, the Princess knew very little of that wise woman's garden other than the nature and the location of her garden tools.

o make matters worse, the Wizard seemed totally unsympathetic as she walked away saying only, "Stay in your garden until you find the one there who will teach you what you need to know and give you what you want."

The Wizard did not give me what
I sought.
Could I have failed again?

he Princess sat on a bench and examined her garden. Although it looked better than it had in years, and even though she felt a bit more secure with a garden wall and a gate in place, she still didn't know what she was supposed to do. She wondered what she could possibly do to find what she wanted— someone to take care of her.

At that, the Princess heard a cry and noticed that a small child was seated in the midst of the garden. When she asked the child where she came from, the child replied that she had been placed there many years ago by a spell cast by a King and a Queen. The child complained that she was getting very tired of being a little girl with no one to protect or care for her.

t first, the Princess was not sure what to do. Neither the King, the Queen nor the Prince had taught her to care for the garden of a child. They had only taught her to care for the gardens of adults.

What shall I do?
Who can tell me what to do?
What did I do to deserve this?
Even the Wise Woman Wizard has
abandoned me.

However, when the frightened child held up her hands the Princess recalled that the Wizard had, at least, made her garden safe. She picked up the child and walked all around the garden, showing her the walls and the gate.

And later, when the child cried, the Princess found broth for her to drink and gently rocked her to sleep. Nonetheless, the Princess was not happy. She remained convinced that the Wizard had not understood her request.

lone at last, the Princess of Other People recalled the words of the Wizard and felt her own anger and despair. The magic she once possessed had vanished and would probably never return. The Princess of Other People had lost her Kingdom.

I shall try to care for the child
for there is no one else for me to care for.

n the days that followed the Princess resigned herself to caring for the child. She remembered the ways the Wizard had taught her to study the plants and the soil to see what was needed. She used these methods to begin to care for her own garden and that of the child.

Whenever the Princess ran out of ideas she would venture cautiously out of her garden gate and ask for help from friends and her Ladies-in-Waiting. At other times she would unlock her gates to allow others to come in to help, always careful to deny entry to those who might harm her or trample the tender plants.

How nice to have
a gate and my own key.
I shall take my time and use care
when opening and closing the gate.

s the child grew and the garden prospered the Princess discovered more and more about the wonderful varieties of plants that thrived in her special soil. She also learned to weed out those plants unsuited to her soil and climate. Her quest for knowledge led her to venture out of her garden to find what she needed but kept her so busy that she was forced to teach the child to care for herself. Once released from the magic spell, the child grew rapidly and soon so closely resembled the Princess that passers-by could never tell them apart.

My garden is so different
from the others I have cared for.
There is no one to tell me
if I am doing it right or wrong.
I shall have to rely on the plants
themselves.

The Princess was delighted to discover how easy
it was for her to care for her own garden after so
many years of having to determine what other
people wanted her to do. Therefore, she decided
to share the fruits of her knowledge with others
by writing books on how to cook and garden.

The fruits of her garden became so abundant that
the Princess shared them with the old King and
Queen who, she realized, had never learned to
care for their gardens themselves.

*What a joy to share my bountiful
garden and to live in this lovely place.*

fter many a day, a King from a faraway land came riding by and caught a glimpse of the magnificent garden the Princess had created. He asked her permission to speak to her. She regarded him warily. "Are you seeking someone to tend to your gardens?" she asked.

The King smiled and shook his head. "No, no. I want to care for my own garden and seek a Queen capable of caring for her own garden who can truly share my life with me. Then, and only then, might I be able to live happily ever after."

The Princess relaxed, looked at the King and said, "I will take a careful examination of your garden, and if I like what I see, I may consider joining you as a Queen. However, I shall be very, very careful for, as you may not know, I once was a Princess of Other People and I do not care to hold that title ever again."

"And what," asked the King, "is the title you bear today?"

At that, the former Princess smiled and gazed once more at the grandeur of her garden, "I'm proud today to tell you that the Princess of Other People has now become the Queen of Herself."

It is quite possible that
she lived happily ever after.

A GUIDED JOURNAL

Becoming the Queen of Yourself

PATRICIA R. ADSON, Ph.D. • JENNIFER E. VAN HOMER

INTRODUCTION
Your Guided Journal

The fable of *A Princess and Her Garden* provides a broad framework for the life story of many women (as well as some men). Each of us is born with a unique garden which contains an amazing array of natural resources and potentials that take many years to bear fruit. Like any fable or metaphor, this story is an outline that can be filled in with as many variations as it has readers.

This Journal was created so readers could personalize the Princess story. In these pages you have a chance to reflect deeply on your experience and to record those reflections in the form of a story written and illustrated by you. The structure of this Journal, however, is more than an outline for an autobiography. It also provides you with an opportunity to look back at how and what you learned as well as to look forward to designing a garden that you alone can tend for the rest of your life. Answering the questions in writing gives you a way to revisit your history, describe who you have become, change what needs to be changed, and emerge as the author of your own life story.

The questions asked serve as a guide for you to approach the telling of the story of your life. There is no correct way for you to respond to what has been asked and no two people will approach this task in the same way. Your memories and thoughts are yours alone. No one else can write your story and no one else has the right to critique what you have written. What you share with others is up to you.

Use your skills of creativity and curiosity as you determine how to express yourself. Answer all of the questions or be selective. (Not every question is applicable to every reader but if you decide to skip a question ask yourself why you are doing so.)

Space has been left for you to answer the questions in the Journal but you may find instances where you want to write more than the available space can accommodate. You will find some blank pages at the end of each section to expand on your thoughts or you may even choose to create a separate volume or notebook. Some questions may take a lot of time to answer and will turn into little essays in and of themselves. Some questions will evoke memories that can be delightful or painful. Take your time. Consider this as a long-term project, not one you will want to complete in a few days. Read over your previous work before moving ahead. Write in the way that best expresses yourself. All questions do not have to be answered in the same way. You might find that a picture you draw, combined with prose, expresses more than words alone. Create a collage or write a poem. This Journal is for you. Reflect, enjoy, and learn something valuable about yourself that you can use from now on.

Your guided Journal has four sections:

I. **THEN:** The questions here help you see how and why you learned to care for the gardens of other people. It is about the past. You can use this information to look back, reflect and think about where you stand now compared to where you once were. Use the past as a healthy way to look at lessons learned rather than staying trapped in patterns that are no longer productive.

II. THE IN-BETWEEN: This section also pertains to the past but here the focus is on the way in which you left your childhood, or a particular phase of your life. You look at whether you heard a Call—felt a strong desire to start a new chapter in your life, or faced a Fall—experiencing rejection, abandonment, or major disappointment. Looking back, you can trace the steps you took at the beginning of your journey.

III. NOW: Here you will take a good look at the present and decide what you want to change in order to take charge of your life today. This is where you decide on the things that are important to you so you can design the kind of garden that will nourish you well into the future.

IV. FROM NOW ON: The final section is where the plan you have created solidifies as you design a specific approach for going forward. Here you will decide what you will do to make sure that your garden continues to be well cared for and protected the rest of your life. You will complete a living document, a reference guide that will never be outdated and could never have been written by anyone but you.

AUTHOR'S NOTE: The inspiration for this journal came from my daughter, Jennifer Van Homer. What began as her suggestion to create a process to help the reader turn the story into their own became a co-author collaboration that resulted in great meaning for the two of us. Jennifer's understanding of somatic coaching and knowledge of practices that sustain behavioral changes were indispensable. I am both proud and grateful for her contributions.

SECTION I

THEN

pon her birth the tiny Princess was given a garden—a birthright—carefully prepared, fertilized and seeded with everything she would ever need in all the years to come. This perfect garden awaited only tender, gentle care and protection until the day when she would be able to care for it herself.

As you begin to write in this section of your journal, reflect on and examine how you learned what you learned about the world and the way it works. Through most of your early years you are in a state of dependency—the Princess is unable to care for her garden, the young child is unable to care for herself and is dependent on her caregivers. The caregivers also teach her how the world works and how to survive in the climate and culture into which she was born. Much of what we learned at this stage served us well in the past but may not serve us well when we carry these beliefs into our more adult years.

Here you have the opportunity to uncover some of the beliefs you have about yourself and others that came from the environment into which you were born. You can examine those beliefs in the light of where you are now and see if they are still true for you. Each of us has a different garden, even siblings have different experiences of childhood and emerge from it with varying interpretations of the "world and what wags it." Begin by remembering your childhood and the culture, the climate, and the geography of the "garden" you were given. Remember, this is your description of your own experience. Only you can write this story.

Draw, or describe in writing, the garden you were given at birth and your surroundings in childhood. Consider such questions:

Where was your garden?

_____

_____

_____

_____

_____

_____

_____

_____

_____

_____

What kind of soil and weather conditions were there?

_____

_____

_____

_____

_____

_____

_____

_____

_____

A PRINCESS AND HER GARDEN

Were there other gardens nearby? Did you really have a garden
of your own or did other peoples' gardens impinge on yours?
Were there other siblings or relatives in the home? Did you have
to share a room?

_____

_____

_____

_____

_____

_____

_____

_____

_____

_____

_____

_Who were the caregivers? Was there a King and a Queen? Were
there other caregivers?_

_____

_____

_____

_____

_____

_____

_____

_____

_____

_____

Were the caregivers up to the task (old enough or wise enough for the job)?

_____

_____

_____

_____

_____

_____

_____

_____

_____

_____

_____

Were the caregivers happy to have their own gardens as well as another garden to care for?

_____

_____

_____

_____

_____

_____

_____

_____

_____

_____

_____

_____

Picture the family home, the dinner table, the layout of your house. What did you learn in your early years about privacy and respect for other people?

_____

_____

_____

_____

_____

_____

_____

_____

_____

What early memories do you have? Can you recall living in a time of innocence where you felt safe and cared for by your caregivers, or did you have to struggle to get others to take care of you? If so, how did you go about that?

_____

_____

_____

_____

_____

_____

_____

_____

_____

What were your favorite places in or near your home? Where could you go for privacy and safety?

_____

_____

_____

_____

_____

_____

_____

_____

_____

_____

_____

_____

More thoughts and reflections . . .

_____

_____

_____

_____

_____

_____

_____

_____

_____

_____

I must be careful to learn how to make them happy or they will not take care of my garden. When they are not happy it must be because I have done something wrong in caring for their gardens.

What You Learned in Your Garden

In the story, the Princess learned that when she did certain things she brought forth the anger of the King or the disappointment of the Queen. Her immediate response was, "What did I do wrong?" She learned to tailor her behavior to the needs of their gardens, rather than the needs of her own. She based her decisions on what worked for them and made them happy or kept them from being angry and punishing her. In this way she learned that it was her job to please the King and Queen and take care of their feelings. She took this job very seriously.

It is possible that the King and Queen thought they were preparing the Princess for her best future by teaching her to care for their gardens so that she would learn to care for the garden of a future Prince. It may not have occurred to them that as time went by they were not teaching her to care for herself. It is also possible that they may have been thoughtless, overwhelmed, intentionally cruel, or self-centered. No matter what reason, as you answer these questions, focus on yourself and your experience in your early years. Discover how you learned what you learned rather than evaluating your parents' childrearing skills or philosophy.

What was the climate in your garden? Was it predictable or stormy and unpredictable? What flourished there? What perished there?

_____

_____

_____

_____

_____

_____

_____

_____

_____

_____

_____

_____

_____

_____

_____

_____

_____

What role were you assigned or did you assume in the family?
Do you currently play that same role?

_____

_____

_____

_____

_____

_____

_____

_____

_____

_____

In your mother's garden:
What was rewarded and punished in the Queen's garden?

_____

_____

_____

_____

_____

_____

_____

_____

_____

_____

_____

What was valued in the Queen's garden and what was scorned?

_____

_____

_____

_____

_____

_____

_____

_____

_____

_____

_____

What messages did you hear, spoken or unspoken, from the Queen?

_____

_____

_____

_____

_____

_____

_____

_____

_____

_____

_____

_____

The good things about the Queen's messages were . . .

_____

_____

_____

_____

_____

_____

_____

_____

_____

_____

_____

The bad things about the Queen's messages were . . .

_____

_____

_____

_____

_____

_____

_____

_____

_____

_____

_____

_____

In your father's garden:

What was rewarded and what was punished in the King's garden?

_____

_____

_____

_____

_____

_____

_____

_____

_____

_____

_____

What was valued in the King's garden and what was scorned?

_____

_____

_____

_____

_____

_____

_____

_____

_____

_____

_____

_____

What messages did you hear in his garden?

_____
_____
_____
_____
_____
_____
_____
_____
_____
_____
_____
_____

The good things about the King's messages were . . .

_____
_____
_____
_____
_____
_____
_____
_____
_____
_____
_____
_____
_____
_____

The bad things about the King's messages were . . .

_____

_____

_____

_____

_____

_____

_____

_____

_____

_____

_____

_____

_____

Look how my garden thrives when I do as they want. Now I have learned my job. I am the Princess of Other People after all—their happiness and mine are intertwined in our gardens.

Summing up: Looking Back on Your Garden, Now and Then

Look at your life today. Ask yourself how you continue to care for the gardens of the King and the Queen (and others) in order to get them to care for your garden or understand and appreciate you. Answer these questions and decide what beliefs and practices you want to retain and what you can let go of.

What did you learn about feelings in your family?

_____

_____

_____

_____

_____

_____

_____

_____

_____

_____

_____

_____

_____

What are your beliefs about making people angry or people making you angry, or making people sad or disappointing others?

_____

_____

_____

_____

_____

_____

_____

_____

_____

_____

_____

What are your beliefs about happiness? Who is responsible for your happiness?

_____

_____

_____

_____

_____

_____

_____

_____

_____

_____

What beliefs did you form about how a relationship works? Do you still hold the same beliefs?

_____

_____

_____

_____

_____

_____

_____

_____

_____

_____

_____

What beliefs and practices do you want to keep from your
childhood experience and what do you no longer need?

_____

_____

_____

_____

_____

_____

_____

_____

_____

_____

_____

What did you love to do as a child?

_____

_____

_____

What did you want to be when you grew up?

_____

_____

_____

What happened to those dreams?

_____

_____

_____

More thoughts and reflections . . .

More thoughts and reflections . . .

More thoughts and reflections . . .

SECTION II
THE IN-BETWEEN

Unfortunately, in a very short while, all of her satisfaction drained away and the Princess was filled with a vast emptiness. "What now?" she asked herself as she returned to her own parched and wilted garden. "How can I ever find anyone to care for me now?"

In sorrow and bewilderment the Princess wandered alone, seeking someone who might help her to make others understand and appreciate her and care for her garden again.

The Call

Leaving home, forming new relationships, leaving old relationships, or changing careers can be adventures, life-saving escapes, and/or many things in between. Whether we view these turning points in our lives as necessary parts of the maturation process, calamities, or awakenings to new ways of being it helps to reflect on them so that we can gain clarity about our roles and what we learned of ourselves in the process.

At various times in life we may seem to feel a "Call." We sense a deeply felt need to make a change or follow a new path. In the developmental journey through life, the Call signals the beginning of the journey out of dependency. Often we hear it when it is time to leave home. At other times it may mean making life changes in order to follow a dream. If this applies to situations at any time in your life, answer the following questions. If not, skip to the section on the "Fall."

How did you experience a Call?

_____

_____

_____

_____

_____

_____

_____

_____

_____

_____

_____

What was your belief about how to answer that Call and take your journey?

_____

_____

_____

_____

_____

_____

_____

_____

_____

_____

_____

_____

_____

_____

When you were an adolescent what did you want to do with your future life? What were your dreams for yourself?

_____

_____

_____

_____

_____

_____

_____

_____

_____

_____

_____

What obstacles did you have to overcome to meet the Call so that you could reach your destination?

_____

_____

_____

_____

_____

_____

_____

_____

_____

_____

_____

_____

How did the King and the Queen help you to find your way?

_____

_____

_____

_____

_____

_____

_____

_____

_____

_____

_____

_____

In what ways did they hinder you?

_____

_____

_____

_____

_____

_____

_____

_____

_____

_____

_____

_____

What is life calling you to do right now? Do you allow yourself to listen to the Call?

_____

_____

_____

_____

_____

_____

_____

_____

_____

_____

Have there been Calls that you ignored? At what cost?

_____

_____

_____

_____

_____

_____

_____

_____

_____

_____

_____

_____

I've done it again, she cried. I am a failure. If only I knew more. I have lost all of my power to make others happy and now know only how to make them sad and angry. It is all my fault. I am not a very good Princess.

The Fall

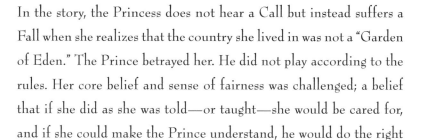

In the story, the Princess does not hear a Call but instead suffers a Fall when she realizes that the country she lived in was not a "Garden of Eden." The Prince betrayed her. He did not play according to the rules. Her core belief and sense of fairness was challenged; a belief that if she did as she was told—or taught—she would be cared for, and if she could make the Prince understand, he would do the right thing.

Sometimes, a Fall does not occur for many years, perhaps even after a first Call has been answered. No matter when it occurs or how severe it is, we must respond to situations that challenge our beliefs or risk remaining trapped in a dependent state. We often hear people blaming their parents or their past for a lack of success many years after they have left home with statements such as "I can't do that because my parents never allowed me to or never gave me the opportunity." Such people remain stuck in the past. On the other hand, some who were overindulged and handed everything in life may retain a sense of entitlement and stay stuck in the past as well. Neither group has learned to take care of themselves. Each lives by a set of rules for a game that no longer exists.

If you had a very painful childhood, you experienced the Fall early in life and this section may be difficult for you to work through. Keep in mind that you want to focus on how you survived your childhood (or traumatic experience) rather than how you were victimized by it. The purpose here is to notice how you developed the strength to surmount life's difficulties, not for you to reexperience the pain. You are in charge and do not need to make yourself miserable.

What was your first realization that things were not as they seemed?

_____

_____

_____

_____

_____

_____

_____

_____

How did you experience the breaking of trust, rejection, or abandonment?

_____

_____

_____

_____

_____

_____

_____

_____

_____

_____

_____

What was your response or reaction? What did you think about yourself? Did you seek revenge?

_____

_____

_____

_____

_____

_____

_____

_____

_____

_____

_____

_____

At the time, what were your beliefs about yourself when you experienced rejection?

_____

_____

_____

_____

_____

_____

_____

_____

_____

_____

What strengths did you draw on to get your life back on track after you experienced a breach of trust, rejection, or abandonment?

_____

_____

_____

_____

_____

_____

_____

_____

_____

_____

_____

More thoughts and reflections . . .

More thoughts and reflections . . .

SECTION III
NOW

Her quest for knowledge led her to venture out of her garden to find what she needed but kept her so busy that she was forced to teach the child to care for herself.

In this section you take on the gardening tasks that enable you to become the "Queen of Yourself."

This is the time of life when we realize at last that our primary responsibility is to care for ourselves and not simply to please and take care of others. In order to do this we take on the complicated task of emotional self-care. The self-care concept is difficult for many to grasp as we view it as a question of "either/or" rather than "both/and." Some equate self-care with physical self-care alone—a vital task but not the only task involved.

Work slowly as you move through this section to free yourself from other people's expectations and become the author and director of your own life story rather than a character in a play written and directed by someone else. Answering the questions in this section will give you an opportunity to practice emotional self-care and reduce your dependence on others.

It is never too late to claim your individuality. No matter when you do it, be aware that it will take courage to face those who will deny your right to be yourself—even if they are long gone from your life.

This process has two parts: identifying the weeds, and then clearing them out and maintaining the garden. We will first identify the weeds of resentment, rejection, and regret. Next we will look at the ways in which you can care for the garden using the tools of forgiveness, creating boundaries, and learning to identify and nourish the crops that grow best there (self-care).

As the child grew and the garden prospered the Princess discovered more and more about the wonderful varieties of plants that thrived in her special soil. She also learned to weed out those plants unsuited to her soil and climate.

Identifying the Weeds

After the Princess lashed out at the gardens of the Prince and the King and the Queen, she found herself alone in a garden choked full of weeds and badly neglected. She had no idea how to care for it. In her despair she sought help from a Wizard who began the process of teaching her the elements of do-it-yourself gardening. The first gardening task was to clear out the weeds.

Before we begin to clear the weeds, however, we must first learn to identify them—to distinguish the weeds from the flowers. The weeds in your garden are all the things that take space in your life and your mind and use up the energy and time you require to live your life to the fullest.

Listen to your self-talk and reflect on your images and your thoughts. Pay attention to the drama playing out in your mind and the stories you are telling yourself about yourself and others. Do you take the lead in this drama or are you a supporting player?

Identifying Resentments. Note that the Princess resented her parents for not teaching her to care for her garden. When your garden is full of weeds (such as resentments), they can crowd out the growth of your happiness through the time and energy you spend thinking about other people who betrayed you, let you down, or did not take care of you. In doing so you neglect your own garden. While it is natural to be resentful, it is not helpful or healthy to hold on to those resentments over long periods of time.

What resentments take up space in your mind?

_____

_____

_____

_____

_____

_____

_____

_____

_____

_____

_____

_____

How much time do you spend having imaginary conversations or focusing on the behavior or motives of other people?

_____

_____

_____

_____

_____

_____

_____

_____

_____

_____

_____

_____

_____

Notice how often you do this in the course of a day. Describe the circumstances that lead you to mutter to yourself after conversations with other people. Describe the thoughts that rattle around in your head about treatment you received or didn't receive, or people who wronged you.

_____

_____

_____

_____

_____

_____

_____

_____

Identifying Rejection. There is no doubt that the Princess was rejected and was deeply affected by the experience. When the Princess was betrayed, she first turned to her Ladies-in-Waiting for advice and help. Their advice was to lash out against those who had betrayed or misled her. This, too, is a natural first response and reaction to rejection and betrayal; however, as the Princess discovered, revenge and retribution do not serve us well and can leave us with feelings of despair.

Although the Princess had experiences of rejection that were both dramatic and obvious, there are numerous less obvious events that we often perceive as rejection. No one can say that another should or should not feel rejected. The essential thing we can change, however, is how we act on that feeling—how we cope with rejection in whatever form we perceive it.

Remember, rejection breeds resentment and when you are full of resentment and anger toward others, you are spending a lot of time in their gardens. In this case you are not caring for their gardens but neither are you caring for your own. In essence, you have abandoned or rejected yourself!

How do past experiences of betrayal, rejection, or abandonment
affect your life today? Are the dead weeds of rejection still taking
up space in your garden? In what way? Name some of the weeds
of rejection in your garden.

_____

_____

_____

_____

_____

_____

_____

_____

_____

_____

_____

_____

What is your typical reaction to rejection?

_____

_____

_____

_____

_____

_____

_____

_____

_____

_____

_____

What do you experience as rejection? For instance, do you feel rejected if someone says no to your ideas, or does it take much more for you to feel rejected? What kind of situations cause you to feel rejected?

_____

_____

_____

_____

_____

_____

_____

_____

_____

Do you ever think of getting even or getting revenge?

_____

_____

_____

_____

_____

_____

_____

_____

_____

_____

_____

Does your fear of rejection prevent you from asking for what you want: for instance, applying for a job, trying out for a part in a play, or being fully present in a relationship?

_____

_____

_____

_____

_____

_____

_____

_____

_____

_____

What stories do you tell yourself about rejection?

_____

_____

_____

_____

_____

_____

_____

_____

_____

_____

_____

_____

_____

Identifying Regrets. Another weed commonly found in the garden is that of regret. Regret is a bit different from resentment or rejection as it refers to things we have done or choices we have made ourselves rather than what others have done or not done to us. Some regret is necessary in life if we are to make changes and learn from our mistakes. Holding on to regret without taking any actions to change, however, crowds out the flowers—what needs to be done today—and keeps us living in the past.

Is your garden full of regrets? What are your thoughts about the unfairness of life or of choices that you made or didn't make?

_____

_____

_____

_____

_____

_____

_____

_____

_____

_____

_____

_____

_____

_____

_____

_____

What regrets crowd out the healthy plants in your garden? How much time do you spend ruminating about them? Is this useful to you?

_____

_____

_____

_____

_____

_____

_____

_____

_____

_____

Under what circumstances do you find yourself spending time thinking about how you could have acted differently in the past?

_____

_____

_____

_____

_____

_____

_____

_____

_____

_____

_____

_____

When thinking of difficult times in the past, do you focus on others and their treatment of you and how they have wronged you, or are you more likely to blame yourself?

_____

_____

_____

_____

_____

_____

_____

_____

_____

_____

_____

How do you cope with regret?

_____

_____

_____

_____

_____

_____

_____

_____

_____

_____

She remembered the ways the Wizard had taught her to study the plants and the soil to see what was needed. She used these methods to begin to care for her own garden and that of the child.

Garden Maintenance

Now that you have identified the weeds, you can look at ways to get rid of them and tend to the garden that is yours to keep. Cleaning up the garden and getting rid of the weeds is a process that only you can do. Even though the Princess turned to the Wizard for help in learning to use the tools, it was only after the Wizard left her on her own, that she fully assumed the task of master gardener.

Tending the garden involves learning to monitor your thoughts and reflect on your actions, then letting go, forgiving, creating boundaries, and caring for the most tender and sensitive parts of your being: the inner child. In the book, the concept of the inner child appears as the young child in the garden. In our lives, the inner child is the name we give to the part of ourselves that hears us when we talk to ourselves and tells us—without words—what we need and what we fear.

How you talk to yourself when you experience resentment, rejection, or regret affects your ability to clean up your own garden. This is another do-it-yourself chore, not one you can hire out. The following are suggestions to try when you find weeds in your garden. They all require developing practices to monitor and reflect on your thoughts and change your focus from others to yourself.

Gardening Tools and Techniques

There are several gardening techniques and tools we can use to clear the weeds of resentment, rejection, and regret. These include forgiveness, building and maintaining boundaries, self-care, and asking for help.

Forgiveness. The purpose of forgiving others is one that rids your garden of time-consuming resentments. Some people have trouble with the word forgiveness because it feels like they are letting someone off the hook. But forgiveness doesn't mean excusing the offending behavior. If the word forgiveness bothers you, think of it as letting go. The Princess didn't excuse the Prince but she let go of her focus on him and instead began to take care of herself. Think about how much time you will have when you put down the burden of carrying around someone else's wrongdoing.

Is there someone you need to forgive or let go of (not excuse) so you can get on with your life?

_____

_____

_____

_____

_____

_____

_____

_____

_____

_____

_____

How will your life change if you can do this?

_____

_____

_____

_____

_____

_____

_____

_____

_____

_____

_____

_____

What do you need to forgive yourself for?

_____

_____

_____

_____

_____

_____

_____

_____

_____

_____

_____

Where in your life do you need to have compassion and forgiveness
for yourself so the regrets don't crowd out the healthy plants?

_____

_____

_____

_____

_____

_____

_____

_____

_____

_____

_____

Is there anyone whose forgiveness you need to ask? How will that help you clear out the weeds and let go of your regrets?

_____

_____

_____

_____

_____

_____

_____

_____

_____

_____

_____

_____

If you were to let go of resentment and regret by focusing on something you could do something about, what would that be?

_____

_____

_____

_____

_____

_____

_____

_____

_____

_____

How can you continue to remember the practices you need to attend to daily? Without constant attention, the weeds may grow back.

_____

_____

_____

_____

_____

_____

_____

_____

Creating Boundaries. The Wizard gave the Princess many tools and much assistance. The Wizard's most important help was showing the Princess how to create a garden wall and install a gate with a key to assist her with maintaining boundaries. The Princess benefited from the Wizard's help, but finally the time came for her to deal with the garden on her own and learn to trust her own judgment.

Our personal boundaries are an important part of becoming individuals and learning to live in society. That these boundaries are ours to maintain is a lesson many of us do not learn easily. In childhood we are not in charge of our own boundaries. We need others to protect us and keep us from harm. We spend lots of time teaching children about the ideas of boundaries but many adults have not learned to maintain their own territorial integrity or to respect that of their neighbors.

People violate boundaries in many ways. This may take the form of asking intrusive questions, getting too close physically, or at the worst, engaging in some type of abuse. In cases of physical boundary violation (such as rape), we often need to call on support from others to maintain physical safety. In emotional boundary violation, however, there is no one to call on but ourselves.

Like the other gardening tools, boundary maintenance is a lifelong job that requires regular practice. Emotional boundary keeping requires knowing where you stand, knowing what you want, and the ability to say "no" and mean it regardless of the reaction of other people. Being able to do this gracefully is an art. We frequently avoid it by complaining about others, focusing on others rather than ourself, not being clear about what we want or are asking (instead, expecting that others should know), and not standing firm. In short, we spend more time in the gardens of others than we do in our own.

Describe (or draw) the state of your garden wall. What does it look like? Is it a picket fence or a cement, fortress-like wall? Are there openings in the wall or places where it is weak? What does the gate look like and who holds the key?

_____

_____

_____

_____

_____

_____

_____

What do YOU need to do to maintain your garden wall?

_____
_____
_____
_____
_____
_____
_____
_____
_____

Who and what do you want inside your garden and who do you want to keep outside? When you let someone in, are you capable of asking them to leave if you no longer want them there?

_____
_____
_____
_____
_____
_____
_____
_____
_____

How vulnerable is your wall? Do you allow some people to come in before you know that you can trust them?

_____

_____

_____

_____

_____

_____

_____

_____

_____

_____

_____

Do you state what you want clearly or do you grumble to others about a personal infraction rather than addressing the offending behavior with the person involved?

_____

_____

_____

_____

_____

_____

_____

_____

_____

_____

What do you need to do to make your boundaries stronger?

_____

_____

_____

_____

_____

_____

_____

_____

_____

What happens when you want to say no? What thoughts and stories come to mind about standing firm and speaking up for yourself?

_____

_____

_____

_____

_____

_____

_____

_____

_____

_____

_____

What happens when you want to say yes? How do you sabotage yourself and how do you take responsibility for yourself?

_____

_____

_____

_____

_____

_____

_____

_____

_____

Your Own Boundary Violations: Tending the Gardens of Others. As a young child the Princess had to learn to tend the gardens of the King and Queen—a natural process faced by most of us as we grow up. As adults, however, we sometimes forget that we can make ourselves miserable by spending too much time in the gardens of others.

We tend other people's gardens by worrying about what they will think of us or by putting their needs and expectations ahead of ours. We say things such as "I can't do that or they will think less of me." Or "If I speak up they will use what I say against me." We need to take others into account and to consider their possible reactions and feelings, but if our focus is always outward we neglect ourselves. Statements such as these are made from the point of view of the other, not from the inside of the self.

In what ways do you trespass on other people's gardens?

_____

_____

_____

_____

_____

_____

_____

_____

_____

_____

How would you like to change this?

_____

_____

_____

_____

_____

_____

_____

_____

_____

_____

_____

_____

Identifying and Nourishing the Special Gifts of the Garden. The Princess said, "I shall care for the child for there is no one else to care for her." It is important to note that she learned to care for the "inner child" by closely observing the child and learning to identify her needs rather than following the patterns used by her parents or doing the opposite of her parents. The Princess used the child as her guide.

Children are instinctively aware of the sensations of physical pain or pleasure, but they can only learn to name their emotions by observing others' reactions when their emotions are displayed. Many children become so well-versed in observing others' emotions that they are not quite aware of, or in touch with, their own. In the most extreme cases of child abuse, children become numb to their own emotions while being hypervigilant to the emotional states of others. Something like this might have happened to the Princess when the King trampled her garden. At that point she learned to take care of his anger but somehow failed to learn how to respond to her own.

Do you know what your "inner child" needs? How do you care for the child within?

_____

_____

_____

_____

_____

_____

_____

How aware are you of your bodily sensations and emotions?

_____

_____

_____

_____

_____

_____

_____

_____

_____

How do you talk to yourself and/or comfort yourself? Think of what works and what doesn't when things go wrong. Practice talking to yourself in a helpful and constructive way, rather than in a self-critical way.

_____

_____

_____

_____

_____

_____

_____

_____

_____

What practices do you use to cultivate awareness, sharpen your senses, and focus your thoughts? What daily routines or spiritual practices do you use to bring the mind and body into alignment, for example, centering, meditation, journaling, yoga, solitude, prayer, or quiet?

_____

_____

_____

_____

_____

_____

_____

_____

_____

_____

_____

When something goes wrong, how do you handle it?

_____

_____

_____

_____

_____

_____

_____

_____

_____

_____

_____

If you talk to yourself do you make excuses, scold yourself, treat yourself with respect, or take another approach?

_____

_____

_____

_____

_____

_____

_____

_____

_____

When you become aware of your emotions, do you own how you feel? If your feelings are confusing do you try to figure them out, or do you brush them off and try to make them go away?

_____

_____

_____

_____

_____

_____

_____

_____

_____

What are your beliefs about taking action related to your own emotions rather than reacting to other people's emotional states?

_____

_____

_____

_____

_____

_____

_____

_____

_____

_____

_____

Why, or in what circumstances, do you feel entitled to be cared for by others? When you need this how do you go about getting it?

_____

_____

_____

_____

_____

_____

_____

_____

_____

_____

_____

_____

When others take care of you, what is the cost to you? What do you have to give up to get others to take care of you? Can you afford this?

_____

_____

_____

_____

_____

_____

_____

_____

_____

_____

_____

_____

_____

_____

_____

_____

_____

Asking for Help

Not all of those we turn to for help can give us the help we need. The Ladies-in-Waiting may have meant well but taking their advice gave the Princess only momentary satisfaction. When she found the Wizard—although she did not initially recognize or appreciate the Wizard as a mentor—the Princess began to discover how to maintain and protect her own garden.

To whom do you turn for help? What do you expect of others when you ask for help?

_____
_____
_____
_____
_____
_____
_____
_____
_____
_____
_____
_____

What advice from others has proved useful to you in the past?

_____
_____
_____
_____
_____
_____
_____
_____
_____
_____
_____

How helpful are you to others who seek your counsel?

_____
_____
_____
_____
_____
_____
_____
_____
_____

As you survey your garden ask yourself in what domains of your life are you dependent on others to care for you: financial, spiritual, physical, relationships, community, identity, etc.?

_____
_____
_____
_____
_____
_____
_____
_____
_____
_____
_____
_____

Is there anything you choose to do about the ways you are dependent on others?

_____

_____

_____

_____

_____

_____

_____

Self Portrait. Now that you have identified and cleared the weeds, take stock of what is flourishing in your garden. Use the following questions to create a portrait of yourself. Add questions of your own and expand on the picture of yourself as fully as you can.

Identify what flourishes and grows well in your garden. Describe what you love and care about.

_____

_____

_____

_____

_____

_____

_____

List your passions and desires.

_____

_____

_____

_____

_____

_____

_____

_____

_____

_____

List your values.

_____

_____

_____

_____

_____

_____

_____

_____

_____

_____

_____

_____

_____

_____

Are there any situations in which you keep yourself from acknowledging and acting on these values, and if so, describe the person you would be if you acted on these values?

_____

_____

_____

_____

_____

_____

_____

_____

_____

_____

_____

Summarize the previous work by filling in the following with as many answers as you can think of.

My inner strengths are . . .

_____

_____

_____

I have compassion for . . .

_____

_____

_____

I take great joy in . . .

_____

_____

_____

I love . . .

_____

_____

_____

I am good at . . .

_____

_____

_____

I have a unique gift for . . .

_____

_____

_____

I value . . .

_____

_____

_____

I believe I am destined for (called to) . . .

_____

_____

_____

More thoughts and reflections . . .

More thoughts and reflections . . .

SECTION IV

FROM NOW ON

The Princess was delighted to discover how easy it was for her to care for her own garden after so many years of having to determine what other people wanted her to do. Therefore, she decided to share the fruits of her knowledge with others by writing books on cooking and how to garden.

Gardening is a lifelong task. If neglected, weeds can grow and healthy plants can die. Walls can crumble and without our constant tending we can lose the ground we fought so hard to nurture and care for. The Princess thought she knew all she needed to know when she declared herself the Princess of Other People, but she was wrong. Now she sees that if she is to continue as the Queen of Herself, she will have to remain aware of the continuing change in the needs of the garden and do what is required to maintain its integrity.

In this section you get a chance to landscape your own garden. The design credit is yours and the responsibility for maintaining it is yours as well. Obviously, no one can do it all alone; however the ways in which you engage others to help and the ways in which you help and cooperate with others determine whether you will be the Princess of Other People or the Queen of Yourself.

Draw or describe the garden you want for the future. What will flourish there?

_____

_____

_____

_____

_____

_____

_____

_____

_____

What is your territory? You know you have responsibility for yourself and your own happiness but surely you have responsibilities for some others as well. Where do your responsibilities lie outside yourself?

_____
_____
_____
_____
_____
_____
_____
_____
_____
_____

What will you need to import from other gardens? What skills and techniques or tools do you plan to acquire and put to use?

_____
_____
_____
_____
_____
_____
_____
_____
_____
_____
_____

*Describe a situation in your life right now where you need to ask
for help. How do you react or respond when you ask for help and
don't get it?*

_____

_____

_____

_____

_____

_____

_____

_____

_____

*How do you act when you do get the help you need? Can you
receive as well as give?*

_____

_____

_____

_____

_____

_____

_____

_____

_____

_____

_____

What legacy do you want your garden to represent?

_____

_____

_____

_____

_____

_____

_____

_____

_____

_____

Look again at your garden and identify your special gifts. What are your special gifts (the special crops that grow well in your garden that may not grow well in the gardens of others)? Which of these gifts do you need to share with the community or the world? What does your garden add to the greater community of gardens?

_____

_____

_____

_____

_____

_____

_____

_____

_____

Now that you have a better sense of what you want your garden to look like, are there more things you need to learn? If so, what are they?

_____

_____

_____

_____

_____

_____

_____

_____

_____

Now that you see you have a choice and you have developed the intention to use other tools, what do you need to change? What are some of the changes you want to make so you can make the best use of all that grows in your garden? Are you ready to share the fruits of your labor with others, and if so, who are these people?

_____

_____

_____

_____

_____

_____

_____

_____

If you could ask anyone at all, who would you choose to be your mentor and inspiration?

_____

_____

_____

_____

_____

_____

_____

_____

_____

_____

Choose anyone, living or dead, real or fictional, you could look to for guidance in each of the major areas of your life. Why would you choose these people?

_____

_____

_____

_____

_____

_____

_____

_____

_____

_____

Part of the joy of a garden is just being in it and reveling in the sights, sounds, and smells. What do you appreciate and enjoy about your garden just as it is?

_____

_____

_____

_____

_____

_____

_____

_____

_____

You'll know you have learned to care for your own garden when you respond in the following ways:

When people try to climb over the wall or open the gate without asking permission, I will . . .

_____

_____

_____

_____

_____

_____

_____

_____

_____

When I find weeds that are crowding out healthy plants, I will . . .

_____

_____

_____

_____

_____

When others give me unrequested gardening advice, I will . . .

_____

_____

_____

_____

_____

When I invite others to share in my garden, I will be careful to . . .

_____

_____

_____

_____

_____

When I am angry, agitated, or disappointed, I will . . .

_____

_____

_____

_____

_____

Once the Princess learned to care for her own garden, to nourish and protect it, she could look beyond it at the larger landscape of her life and take her place in the collective community. She shared the gifts of her garden with others and traded them for essentials her garden lacked. She could finally consider again the possibility of sharing her garden with someone else. They would enter into a relationship as equal partners, able to care for their own gardens, share a common one, and express caring and concern for the world outside of their borders.

How does this fable pertain to your life and your future?

_____

_____

_____

_____

_____

_____

Write your own ending to the Princess story. What is possible for you in the future?

_____

_____

_____

_____

_____

_____

More thoughts and reflections . . .

More thoughts and reflections . . .

SUMMARY

Now that you have taken a good look at yourself and your life, consider that you have awakened from the "trance of childhood" and your task is to remain awake and sustain the changes you have made. The word "trance" is used because the dependent state of childhood has often been called a "trance state." When in a trance, we are narrowly focused. As children we had to focus on those we depended on for our survival. The world revolved around us and them. Gradually the voices of parents and caregivers took up residence in our minds and we believed they were our own. In this way, the trance continued long after we had left home and family. Without meaning to, we hypnotized ourselves.

To awaken from the trance we need to open our eyes and see all that is around us and then to look inside with a new perspective. It is our hope that the Princess book has been an opportunity for you to do this. This process, however, is not a one-time exercise. You have found the inner resources you need and now you are charged with tending these resources or you may risk falling back on old habits or default positions.

There is nothing selfish about caring for your own garden. You can still care for, or care about, others. But you also have an obligation to care for your own garden or you will forever be like the Princess when she tried so diligently (and failed) to make the Prince understand. If you fail to tend your own garden, you will keep asking others to care for your garden and will continue to be disappointed when they are unable to do so. You see, it wasn't the Prince who needed to understand, it was the Princess!

Building the garden wall and having a gate with a key is not meant to isolate you, but to keep you safe and maintain your territorial integrity. Once you feel safe, like the Princess, you can cultivate the parts of yourself that you want to share with others. People are not meant to be isolated. We are meant to be responsible for the garden that is ours, share those fruits with others, receive from them in exchange, and to take our rightful place in the community we call home.

What you do from now on will be up to you. There are many practices that will help you maintain your garden such as journaling, meditation (particularly mindfulness meditation), lifelong learning, spiritual work, counseling, coaching, and therapy in groups or individually. You might even form a group of your own with others who have read the book and used the workbook.

Whatever you do, we hope you will take these concepts and vocabulary with you in order to help you realize what is happening when you find you are in someone else's garden, or find you have neglected to maintain a secure garden wall, or recognize the weeds that sprout up when you aren't paying attention.

We hope you will let us know of the creative ways you have used this material so we can share your gifts with others to build a community of Queens and Kings who know how to take responsibility for themselves, yet have the ability to come together as unique individuals who share in each others success and happiness. We can be contacted at **aprincessandhergarden@gmail.com**

A Princess and Her Garden
BOOK CLUB QUESTIONS

The Princess felt she was doing the right thing by putting other people's needs before her own. When you take care of your own needs do you feel guilty or selfish?

———

The Princess was still a young woman when she was forced to care for her own garden. If this had happened later in her life would it have been too late? Is it ever too late to begin to care for oneself?

———

Why do you think the King and the Queen taught the Princess to care for them? What does this story have to teach us about raising children?

———

The Wizard gave the Princess tools, helped her build a fence around her garden, and gave her the only key to the gate. Why, then, did the Princess feel abandoned when the Wizard left? What does it mean to be abandoned?

This is a story about a Princess. How might it have been different (or would it) if it were the story of a Prince?

———

The story ends with "it is possible that she lived happily ever after." What would the Princess have to do to ensure her own happiness? Do you think she married a King? If so, what kind of a relationship might they have had?

———